FUN
AMULETS

MAGIC CHARMS FROM ANCIENT EGYPT

BY
DIANA CRAIG PATCH

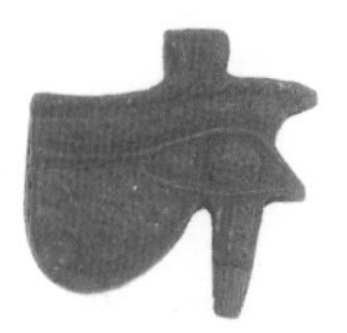

BRITISH MUSEUM PRESS
in association with
THE METROPOLITAN MUSEUM OF ART, NEW YORK

First published in Great Britain in 1997 by British Museum Press
A division of The British Museum Company Ltd
46 Bloomsbury Street, London WC1B 3QQ

ISBN 0-7141-1789-7

All works of art are from the collections of
The Metropolitan Museum of Art.

Produced by the Department of Special Publications,
The Metropolitan Museum of Art

Printed in China

CONTENTS

Amulets in Ancient Egypt
5

About the Amulets
11

How to Make Amulets
35

What to Make with Amulets
44

AMULETS IN ANCIENT EGYPT

In many cultures around the world, people believe that certain shapes, natural objects, or deities have special or magical qualities. When these shapes, objects, or figures are small in size so that they can be hung on the body, they are called amulets. Today, a rabbit's foot can be an amulet; so can a lucky penny or even a special stone. People believe that amulets pass on to the owner the qualities associated with their forms.

The ancient Egyptians called amulets *sa*, their word for protection. They wore them as individual charms and as shapes incorporated into the design of many types of jewelry. They believed that amulets protected them from negative forces or brought good luck. People probably used pebbles, shells, and other natural objects as amulets, but they also wore a variety of shapes made especially for this purpose.

Ancient Egyptian amulets represent deities—in either human or animal form—hieroglyphs, emblems, plants, animals, or ritual objects. Most of these shapes are directly tied to ancient Egyptian religion and symbolize the beliefs that individuals held about their earthly and eternal existence. Most ordinary people spent little time in the temples, and the state religion involved only the king and the priests who acted for him. Amulets were one way that people could personally attempt to control their lives. People hoped to get the

Ipuy displays a *wedjet*-eye necklace and bracelet.
Detail from a facsimile of a wall painting from the tomb of Ipuy
Deir el Medina, Dynasty XIX, reign of Ramesses II
(ca. 1279–1213 B.C.)
Rogers Fund, 1930 30.4.114

magic effects of amulets by wearing them or by leaving them at small, public shrines, perhaps to accompany a prayer to a particular god or goddess.

The Egyptians used amulets in daily life, but one of the most important uses was in funerary rituals. The Egyptians believed that after death, the soul of a person went on a perilous journey to the afterlife. People were buried with many supplies to provide them assistance on the journey. Most of the amulets that survive today were found among this burial equipment, often decorating the owner's body, where their magical qualities helped safeguard the mummy. The *Book of the Dead*, a collection of spells designed to protect the deceased, includes references to amulets and how they should be used.

The ancient Egyptians viewed their entrance into the afterlife as a physical transformation from this life to the next, or in other words, a rebirth. They chose to interpret this event using

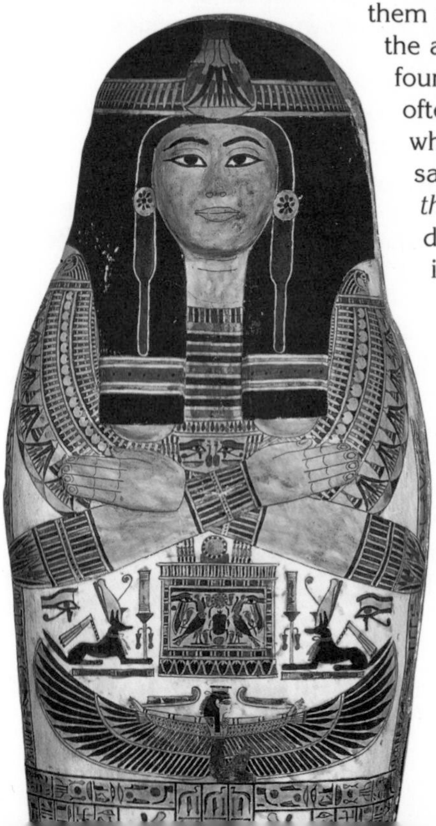

The outer coffin of Henettawy shows funerary jewelry with many amulets.
Thebes, Deir el-Bahri, MMA 59
Dynasty XXI (ca. 1070–945 B.C.)
Wood, gesso, and paint
Rogers Fund, 1925
25.3.182

imagery borrowed from the yearly rejuvenation of the agricultural land caused by the flooding of the Nile River. After the floodwaters receded, the valley turned green, and animals gave birth to their young. Thus, many funerary symbols, such as the color green, papyrus, and frogs (lots were born right after the flood receded), illustrate close ties to fertility or the river.

The ancient Egyptians did not leave many other written records about why they used amulets, so we don't always know what each different form means. In addition, Egyptologists do not always know why the Egyptians assigned certain qualities to particular forms. Some amulets represent specific deities or the animals or symbols associated with the god or goddess, and those can be more easily interpreted. There are some forms that scholars are still trying to understand.

Also, the effectiveness of an amulet may not have resulted just from wearing the form. Some ancient texts indicate that spells were often said over an amulet to make it work. For example, surviving portions of one magical text say, "...I will make...an amulet, their names [certain gods] being pronounced on this day."

Other important factors included color, material, and the way the charm was attached to the body. Certain stones or colors, when used correctly, were believed to make amulets more powerful. In one incantation, the types of stones needed to make the spell work are carefully listed: "This spell must be said over lapis lazuli, turquoise, carnelian, *shert*-stone, malachite, feldspar, granite, *pagau*-stone, and all precious stones and washed with milk." Some of the amulets surviving today are made from semiprecious stones. Many others are made of colored glass or a man-made material called faience.

Amulets have often been found strung on cords that have knots in them. A knot is another method for making the words of a spell effective: The knots tie the words to the object. A number of spells state the importance of knot tying. For example, one says, "Say this spell over a rush soaked in a fermented sop, twisted over the left hand, made into seven knots...."

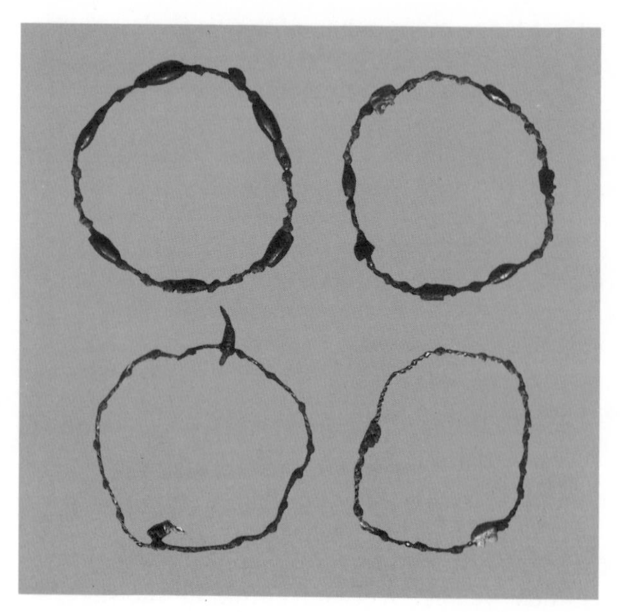

Bracelets found with the burial of Henettawy show the use of knots as well as amulets.
Thebes, Deir el-Bahri, MMA 59
Dynasty XXI (ca. 1070–945 B.C.)
Linen, gold, carnelian, faience, amethyst
Rogers Fund, 1925
25.3.190 A–D

EGYPTIAN CHRONOLOGY

(Dates are approximate.)

Predynastic Period
4500–3100 B.C.

Archaic Period (Dynasties 0–2)
3100–2649 B.C.

Old Kingdom (Dynasties 3–8)
2649–2134 B.C.

First Intermediate Period (Dynasties 9–11)
2134–2140 B.C.

Middle Kingdom (Dynasties 11–13)
2140–1640 B.C.

Second Intermediate Period (Dynasties 14–17)
1640–1550 B.C.

New Kingdom (Dynasties 18–20)
1550–1070 B.C.

Third Intermediate Period (Dynasties 21–24)
1070–712 B.C.

Late Period (Dynasties 25–30)
712–332 B.C.

Macedonian and Ptolemaic Periods
332–30 B.C.

ANCIENT EGYPT

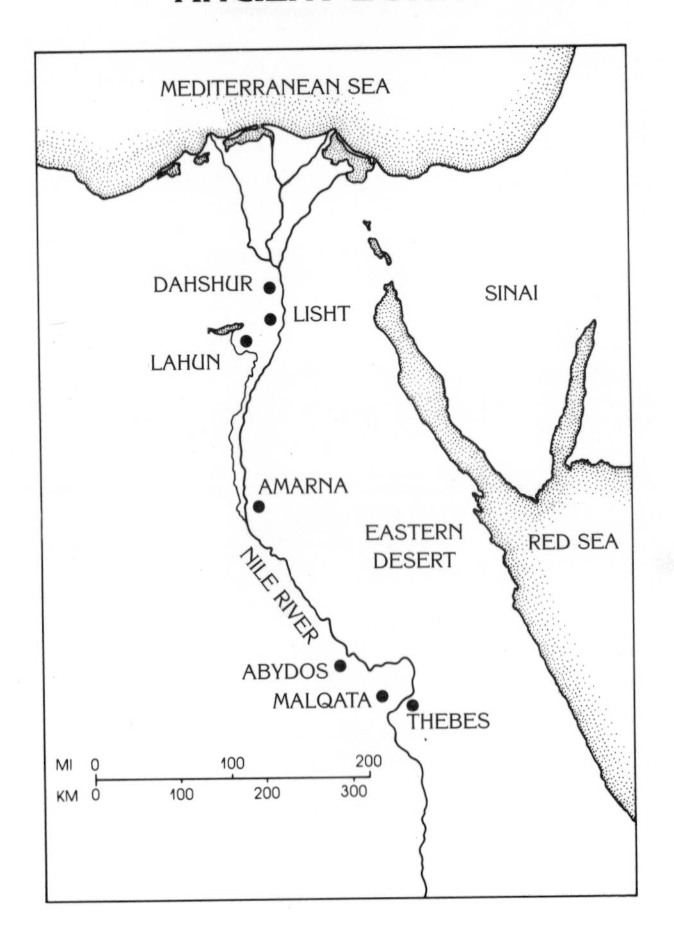

ABOUT THE AMULETS

This kit contains a mold with 24 different amulet forms. Each of the forms is modeled from an actual Egyptian amulet or amulet mold. On the following pages, you'll find information about the ancient amulets and their meaning. Also included are instructions for making your own amulets and suggestions for using them. You can use amulets for decorations or as gifts and charms for different occasions, based on their ancient meanings. As you make the amulets, you'll learn about the ancient Egyptians and the magic and ritual that were so important to their lives.

ANKH

ANKH MOLD
Malqata
Dynasty XVIII, reign of Amenhotep III
(ca. 1391–1353 B.C.)
Ceramic; h. 1 in. (2.7 cm), w. ¾ in. (2.1 cm)
Rogers Fund, 1911
11.215.711

The *ankh* is the hieroglyph meaning life, living, or to live. So an amulet shaped like an *ankh* is designed to give, protect, or extend life. Egyptologists think the *ankh*'s shape might originally have represented a sandal strap or tie. The *ankh* may have been chosen to represent the concept "life" because the word for the object it depicted sounded like the word for life, for which no picture could be drawn.

Ankh amulets were rare. Only a few examples have been found, and most were strung with other amulets in a necklace, rarely alone. There is a strong association between the *ankh* and ancient Egyptian gods and goddesses, and most representations of deities show them carrying an *ankh* in one hand. Because of its close association with the gods, Egyptians may have thought the *ankh* was inappropriate or too potent for most humans to possess.

The Sons of Horus Holding *Ankhs*
Detail from a facsimile of a wall painting from the Tomb of Nebamun and Ipuky
Thebes, Dynasty XVIII, time of Amenhotep II–IV
(ca. 1427–1349 B.C.)
Rogers Fund, 1930
30.4.157

Put an ankh *pendant on a necklace of other amulets or attach an* ankh *to anything that is particularly precious to you. The* ankh *can mean "long life," so you can use it to say "Happy Birthday."*

This baboon probably represents Thoth, the god of wisdom, who was the scribe and record keeper for the gods. Although this one does not wear a crown, many squatting baboon amulets have a crown with a full moon nestled inside a crescent moon. The moons refer to Thoth's role as scribe and keeper of the Egyptian calendar, which was based on a lunar cycle. Such moons can also indicate the moon god, Khonsu.

The Egyptians believed that when the dead person's soul journeyed to the underworld, his or her heart would be weighed against a feather to see if it were innocent of crimes. Only if the heart were lighter than the feather would the soul travel on to paradise. Because Thoth was responsible for weighing the heart, baboons were important funerary amulets.

Baboons were also connected with Re, the sun god. The animals often face the sun to warm themselves in the early morning. To the Egyptians it seemed that they were worshiping the rising sun.

BABOON

SEATED BABOON
Dynasty XXVI (ca. 712–664 B.C.)
Faience; h. 1¼ in. (3.1 cm), w. 11/16 in. (1.6 cm)
Gift of J. Pierpont Morgan, 1917
17.194.2438

Thoth was the god of learning, writing, and measuring. Use baboons to decorate pencils, pencil and pen cases, bookmarks, or rulers. A baboon can be a good luck charm for someone taking a test. There are two molds for the baboon amulet, one for the front and one for the back, so you can put them together to make a three dimensional figure. (Tips are on page 45.) See page 46 to see how to make a pencil or pen top.

BES-IMAGE

BES-IMAGE MOLD
Malqata
Dynasty XVIII,
reign of Amenhotep III
(ca. 1391–1353 B.C.)
Ceramic; h. 1⅝ in. (4.1 cm),
w. 1 3/16 in. (3.0 cm)
Rogers Fund, 1912
12.180.364

A Bes-image can depict one of several gods, but the best known is a male dwarf, called Bes, with the mane, ears, and tail of a lion. The Bes-image has a long history, first appearing in the Old Kingdom in a lionlike form. He became more and more popular through time, soon taking on the form of a dwarf.

The Bes-image was used for amulets and statuettes and on vessels of various types. He was never a major deity in the temples of Egypt but instead was worshiped in households and in small, public shrines. The Bes-image was responsible for protecting the household and its occupants. In particular, he was believed to watch over its most delicate residents, children and pregnant women. Later in Egyptian history, he was often represented dancing and playing musical instruments.

Use the Bes-image amulet to decorate a drum or drumsticks or household containers. Decorate a picture frame with Bes-images as a gift for a new baby. The Bes-image is a protective amulet. Use it on a key ring or to decorate a box where you keep special things.

Spell: "I am Horus who conjures so that she who is giving birth improves as if she were delivered..." To be said four times over a clay dwarf laid on the forehead of the woman who is having a baby.

Another Example of a Bes-image Amulet
Abydos, Tomb D14E, Dynasty XVIII,
reign of Amenhotep II or later
(ca. 1427–1295 B.C.)
Green faience with paste inlay;
h. 3⅛ in. (7.9 cm)
Gift of Egypt Exploration Fund, 1900
00.4.33

CAT

Charms representing a seated cat, sometimes surrounded by her kittens, were most common in the later periods of ancient Egypt. Such cats depict the goddess Bastet, who could also be shown as a woman with a lionlike face.

Bastet was a pleasant-tempered deity associated with fertility, so cat amulets may have had a role in funerary ritual as fertility figures. People may also have left them at small shrines, perhaps after praying to have a baby. Bastet was often shown carrying the musical instruments used in temple rituals, so she also played a role in religious festivities.

Figure of Cat with Eight Kittens
Late Dynastic Period
(ca. 664–343 B.C.)
Faience; h. 2.5 in. (6.4 cm),
w. ½ in. (1.2 cm)
Rogers Fund, 1945
45.2.2

Dynasty XXVI–XXX
(ca. 664–343 B.C.)
Faience; h. 1⅜ in. (3.4 cm),
w. ⅜ in. (.9 cm)
Gift of Helen Miller Gould, 1910
10.130.2004

There are molds for the left and right halves of the cat, so you can put them together. *(See page 45 for tips on making three-dimensional amulets.)*
Use cat amulets to decorate party invitations and place cards. Make pendants or key rings. Hang a cat amulet on your pet's collar. Be sure your pet cat knows there is a cat goddess!

CLAW

CLAW
Abydos, Tomb V21
Dynasty XII (ca. 1971–1783 B.C.)
Silver over wood; h 1 3/16 in. (3.0 cm), w. 11/16 in. (1.7 cm)
Gift of the Egypt Exploration Fund, 1904 04.18.23

Claws are some of the earliest amulet forms known in ancient Egypt, but they are rare. Some of these amulets represent the claw of a leopard and some imitate the talon of a large bird. The basic form of this amulet suggests it is intended to represent the leopard-claw type.

Women appear to have worn pairs of claws around each ankle. Several sets of claw anklets have been found in graves of princesses. One painting shows a dancer wearing claw anklets. The meaning of these amulets is difficult to interpret. Because they are associated with cats, perhaps claws also signified fertility. The instructions for one spell say that it was to be said over the tips of falcon's claws and the shell of a tortoise.

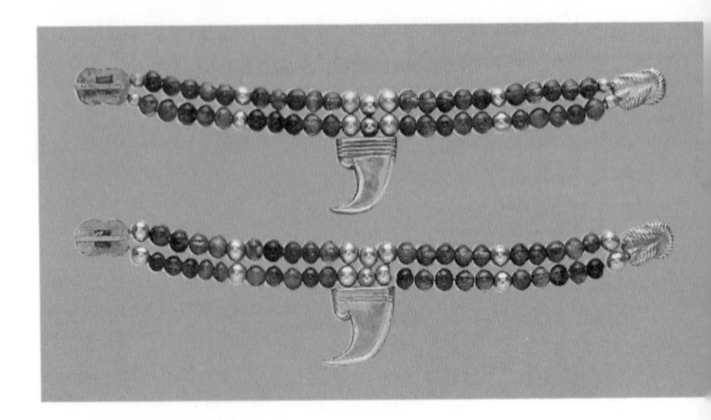

Pair of Anklets with Claws
Lahun, Tomb 8 (Princess Sithathoryunet)
Dynasty XII, reigns of Senwosret II–Amenemhet III (ca. 1897–1797 B.C.)
Gold and amethyst; l. 6 7/8 in. (17.5 cm)
Rogers Fund and Henry Walters Gift, 1916 16.1.7a,b

Make anklets like a princess's, or add a claw pendant to a necklace or a key ring.

COWRIE SHELL

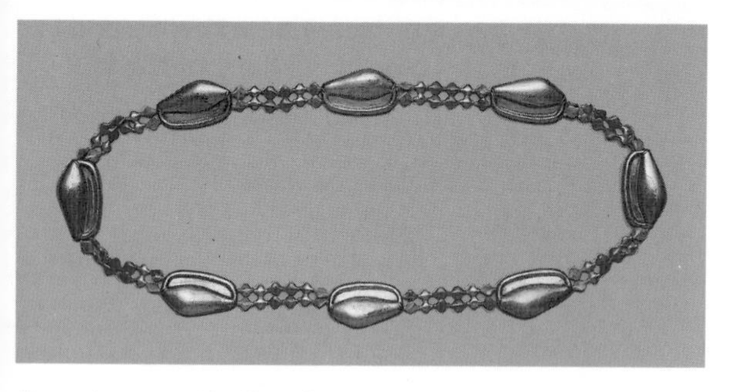

Cowries are shells of common snails that live in the Red Sea. Many East African cultures associated this type of shell with female fertility.

Cowries seem to have been used frequently to decorate women's girdles or hip beads, loose belts of beads worn around the hips. Some girdles used real shells strung together with cord or leather thongs. Others, made for queens, princesses, and other wealthy women, used exquisite imitation cowries of gold or silver linked by small beads made of semiprecious stones. Some metal cowries contain tiny pieces that made a subtle jingling sound when the wearer walked. Representations of girdles are common on young women and therefore may be related to fertility or adolescence.

Cowrie Girdle
Lahun, Dynasty XII (ca. 1897–1797 B.C.)
Gold, carnelian, and green feldspar; l. 33 in. (84 cm)
Rogers Fund and Henry Walters Gift, 1916 16.1.5

COWRIE BEAD
Dahshur, Dynasty XII
(ca. 2061–1640 B.C.)
Gold; h. ⅜ in. (.9 cm),
w. 9/16 in. (1.5 cm)
Rogers Fund, 1911
11.150.52b

Use cowries to decorate a belt or a barrette, or use them with other amulets in a bracelet, necklace, or anklet. Make a cowrie amulet on a jewelry hook, then attach it to an elastic band or hair ribbon for a hair ornament.

CROCODILE

CROCODILE
Early Ptolemaic Period
(ca. 305–247 B.C.)
Faience; l. 1½ in. (3.8 cm)
Gift of Norbert Schimmel Trust, 1989 1989.281.96

For the ancient Egyptians, the crocodile was a frightening inhabitant of the Nile River. Such a dangerous creature could be seen as an animal from which people needed protection or a beast so terrifying that it could ward off evil. Some crocodile amulets represent the solar god Sobek-Re, who usually wore a crown of a sun disk. Other crocodiles were intended to provide protection against a frightening animal or evil in general. One particular spell calls for the words to be recited over a crocodile made of clay with a faience eye and wheat in its mouth.

Glue crocodiles to your sunglasses. Put a crocodile on your bicycle to keep fierce dogs away.

Crocodiles, Frogs, Lions, and Turtle on a Magic Ro
Late Dynasty XII–XIII (ca. 1850–1640 B.C.
Glazed steatite; l. 11 in. (28 cm
Purchase, Edward S. Harkness Gift, 1926 26.7.127

DJED-PILLAR

The *djed*-pillar is associated with Osiris, the ruler of the underworld. Often called Osiris's backbone, the *djed*-pillar may originally have represented a tree with its branches cut off. Its shape stood for stability or permanence when written in ancient Egyptian.

This charm had a purely funerary purpose. It was placed on the mummy to unite the dead person with Osiris. The *Book of the Dead* contains a specific spell that the priest said over the amulet before it was placed upon the dead person during the mummification process.

Spell: "Raise up, O Osiris [the deceased person], lie on your side that I may put water under you and that I may bring you a golden djed-*pillar so that you will be happy."*

DJED-PILLAR
Dynasty XXVI–XXX
(ca. 664–332 B.C.)
Faience; h. 1¾ in. (4.4 cm),
w. ⅝ in. (1.5 cm)
Gift of Joseph W. Drexel, 1889
89.2.539

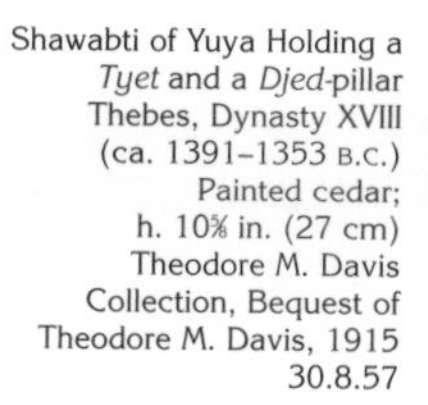

Shawabti of Yuya Holding a
Tyet and a *Djed*-pillar
Thebes, Dynasty XVIII
(ca. 1391–1353 B.C.)
Painted cedar;
h. 10⅝ in. (27 cm)
Theodore M. Davis
Collection, Bequest of
Theodore M. Davis, 1915
30.8.57

The djed-*pillar represents "stability," so use it on a magnet, thumbtack or drawing pin, tie tack, or paperweight. It also means "endurance," so you can use it as a charm for someone running a marathon or studying for a test.*

FISH

BOLTI-FISH MOLD
Tell el-Amarna
Dynasty XVIII, reign of Akhenaten
(ca. 1349–1336 B.C.)
Ceramic; l. 1⅞ in. (4.8 cm),
w. 1⅜ (3.5 cm)
Gift of Edward S. Harkness, 1921
21.9.127

Since the Egyptians lived along the Nile River, fish were an important source of food. But some fish also had roles in religion, like this *Tilapia* fish, commonly called a Bolti, whose reproductive cycle mirrored religious beliefs.

In one subspecies, the female fish gathers her eggs into a large ball on the river bed, protecting them until they hatch. The Egyptians probably observed the ball of eggs producing new fish. They seem to have equated the ball of eggs with the sun, also a ball, from which the Egyptians believed all life sprang. The female fish in another *Tilapia* subspecies holds the eggs inside her mouth until they hatch. Egyptians would have seen this as a form of self-propagation, an important concept in their creation mythology.

Fish-shaped Dish
Dynasty XVIII, reign of Tuthmosis III (ca. 1479–1425 B.C.)
Glazed steatite; l. 7⅛ in. (18.1 cm)
Gift of James Douglas, 1890 90.6.24

Use the fish to decorate a magnet or flowerpots, or to decorate accessories in a bathroom, such as a toothbrush holder or a tissue box. A fish might be a good present for someone who's learning to swim.

FLY

Flies were probably as common in ancient times as they are today. The meaning of fly amulets is not clear, but fertility—flies breed easily—is one interpretation. Another possibility is that people wore fly amulets to ward off the real pests. Most often, several small fly amulets are found strung together on a necklace.

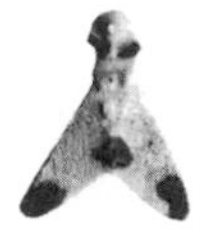

FLY
Lisht, North Pyramid
Middle Kingdom–Second Intermediate Period
(ca. 1991–1550 B.C.)
Faience; l. 9/16 in. (1.4 cm), w. 15/32 in. (1.2 cm)
Rogers Fund and Edward S. Harkness Gift, 1922
22.1.1389

Other Examples of Flies

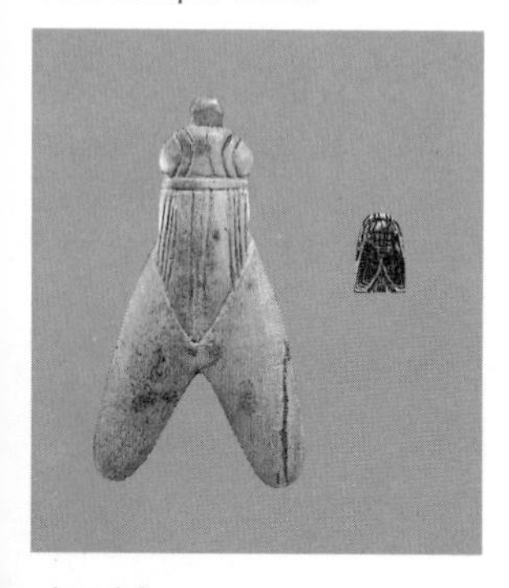

above
Dynasty XXVI–XXIX
(664–380 B.C.)
Faience (?);
l. 7/16 in. (1.2 cm)
Bequest of Mary Anna Palmer Draper, 1915
15.43.47

above left
Dynasty XIII–XVII
(ca. 1783–1550 B.C.)
Ivory; l. 2 7/16 in. (6.3 cm)
Purchase, Edward S. Harkness Gift, 1926
26.7.1285

above right
Early Dynasty XVIII
(ca. 1550–1525 B.C.)
Glazed steatite; l. ½ in. (1.3 cm)
Gift of Helen Miller Gould, 1910
10.130.168

Glue flies to a flyswatter, attach them to a fishing cap, or put a fly on your picnic basket to scare real bugs away from your food!

FROG

TREE FROG
New Kingdom
(ca. 1550–1070/69 B.C.)
Faience; h. ⅜ in. (1.0 cm),
w. ⅜ in. (1.0 cm)
Purchase, Edward S.
Harkness Gift, 1926
26.7.1028

This little amulet depicts a small frog, probably one that lives in trees. Because of the river and surrounding marshlands, the Nile Valley had large numbers of frogs. Their association with a watery habitat and their ability to produce large numbers of offspring made them a perfect symbol for fertility and rebirth, common themes in ancient Egyptian mythology. The frog could represent the goddess Heket, who was depicted in temples attending birthing scenes.

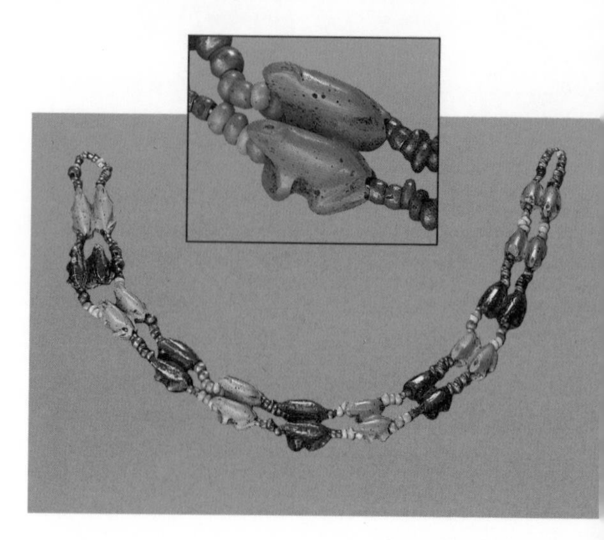

String of Double-Frog Beads
New Kingdom
(ca. 1550–1070/69 B.C.)
Glass; l. 10½ in. (27.4 cm)
Gift of Mrs. Frederick F. Thompson, 1915
15.6.47

Use frogs to decorate a ring. Glue them to bathroom accessories or flowerpots.

HAND AND LEG

These charms depict an open human hand with the fingers close together, and a person's lower leg and foot seen from the side.

Amulets representing hands and feet are most common among early Egyptian burial goods. Egyptologists believe that amulets of body parts were meant to substitute for lost limbs if a dead person needed one in the afterlife. People may also have believed that these charms could give the power of movement and action. Hand and foot amulets were most commonly made in carnelian, a reddish-orange stone. Perhaps Egyptians linked its color to blood and therefore a strong, healthy body.

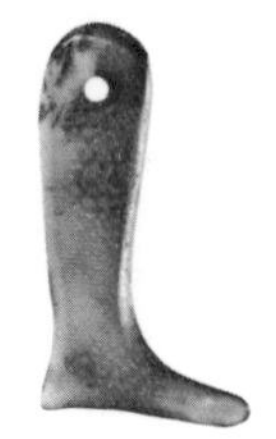

HAND
Dynasty V–XI
(ca. 2465–2134 B.C.)
Carnelian; h. 5/8 in. (1.7 cm),
w. 5/16 in. (.8 cm)
Gift of Helen Miller Gould, 1910
10.130.2358

LEG
Dynasty V–XI
(ca. 2465–2134 B.C.)
Carnelian;
h. 1 1/16 in. (2.6 cm),
w. 9/16 in. (1.4 cm)
Gift of Helen Miller Gould, 1910
10.130.2354

Put hands on a bracelet or ring and legs on an anklet or shoelaces. Try combining them, too. Use a leg amulet as good luck for a sports event, or a hand as good luck for art activities. They can also be "get-well" charms for someone who has injured a hand or foot.

HARE

HARE
Ptolemaic Period (304–30 B.C.)
Faience; l. 1⅜ in. (3.3 cm),
h. ⅞ in. (2.2 cm)
Rogers Fund, 1944
44.4.25

The hare is an unusual amulet form, common only in the later part of Egyptian history. It was the sacred animal of a minor goddess, Wenet, but that is unlikely to be the reason for its use. Like several other amulet types already mentioned—frogs, flies, and cats—the hare was also a fertility symbol, because of the ease with which members of the rabbit family reproduce. The hare's renowned swiftness and sharp senses might have been another reason that people chose to wear it as an amulet.

Attach hare amulets to your shoelaces or sports equipment to encourage you to run as fast as a rabbit.

HEART

The ancient Egyptians believed that the heart was the source of a person's intelligence, thoughts, and feelings. So it was important to protect the heart in a mummy. There are two kinds of heart amulets: large ones, often inscribed with an appropriate spell from the *Book of the Dead*, and small ones like this. Both sizes were employed among funerary equipment.

Spell recited over a heart amulet: "I am the phoenix who is the soul of Re. I guide the gods to the Underworld when they leave. The souls on earth will do what they want and the soul of [the deceased] will leave when he wants."

HEART
Dynasty XX–XXX
(ca. 1186–332 B.C.)
Green stone; h. 1¼ in. (2.9 cm),
w. ¾ in. (2.0 cm)
Gift of Helen Miller Gould, 1910
10.130.1797

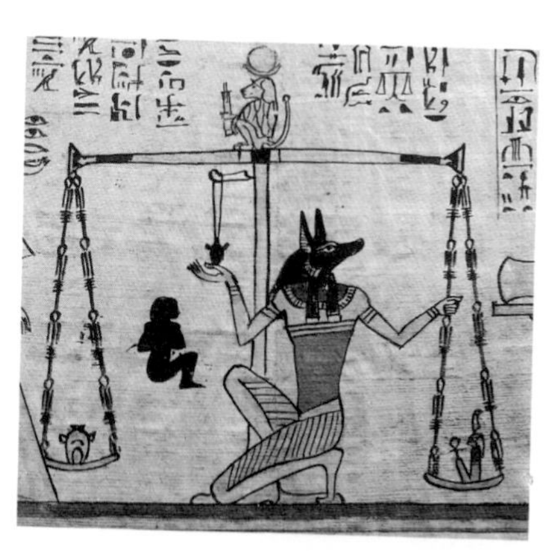

Weighing of the Heart
During Judgment
Detail from Nany's
Funerary Papyri
Dynasty XXI, early in
reign of Psusennes I
(ca. 1040–1020 B.C.)
Thebes, Deir el-Bahri,
SAE 358 (MMA 65)
Papyrus; entire l.
205⅜ in. (521.5 cm),
h. 14 in. (35–35.5 cm)
Rogers Fund, 1930
30.3.31

Add a heart amulet to a pendant, a book bag, or a jewelry box.

IBIS

The ibis is a water bird, similar to the heron. Several ibis species wintered in the Nile Valley, but only one, the sacred ibis, appears to have been revered by the Egyptians. This amulet of an ibis on a perch stands for Thoth, the god of wisdom and scribe of the gods. Thoth was responsible for writing, measuring, and learning. He was often depicted as a man with an ibis head.

IBIS ON A STANDARD
First Intermediate Period
(ca. 2134–2140 B.C.)
Gold; h. ⅞ in. (2.2 cm),
w. ⅝ in. (1.7 cm)
Gift of Helen Miller Gould, 1910
10.130.2064

Statuette of Ibis-headed Thoth
Ptolemaic Period
(304–30 B.C.)
Faience;
h. 5½ in. (14 cm)
Purchase, Edward S. Harkness Gift, 1926
26.7.860

Decorate bookmarks, pencil cases, or rulers so Thoth can inspire you as you do your schoolwork. Give an ibis charm for good luck when taking a test.

SAFETY INSTRUCTIONS

Please read these instructions before use, follow them and keep them for reference

- DO NOT place the material in the mouth
- Contrary to the baking instructions given on pp. 42-3 of the booklet, British safety rules state that you should not exceed a temperature of **130° C** or harmful gases may be produced
- DO NOT exceed a hardening (baking) time of 30 minutes
- The hardening process is not part of the function of the toy and should be carried out by the supervising adult
- Use a domestic oven thermometer, e.g. bimetal, to measure the temperature. DO NOT use a glass thermometer
- DO NOT use a microwave oven
- In case of accidental overheating and inhalation of poisonous gases remove person to fresh air and seek immediate medical advice. In case of doubt seek medical advice without delay. Take the product together with the container with you. In case of injury always seek medical advice.

PAPYRUS SCEPTER

All plants were symbolic of new life, but several had specific roles in religious ritual. This amulet depicts a group of papyrus plants bundled together so that the top looks like a single flower. Since early times in Egypt, papyrus was the symbol of Lower Egypt (the northern section of the country), making the plant a powerful image. Like the heart, *tyet*, and *djed*-pillar, the papyrus scepter helped protect the mummy during its difficult journey into the afterlife.

Spell: "I own a perfect papyrus scepter of green feldspar that the hand of Thoth holds, for he hates injury. If the papyrus scepter stays healthy then I will stay healthy..."

PAPYRUS SCEPTER
Late Period?
(ca. 712–332 B.C.)
Faience; h. 1¾ in. (4.6 cm), diam. 9/16 in. (1.5 cm)
Gift of Joseph W. Drexel, 1889
89.2.538

Decorate flowerpots to encourage flowers to grow. The papyrus scepter is associated with the color green meaning "health," so it makes a good "get-well" gift.

RAM

RAM'S HEAD PENDANT
Dynasty XXV?
(ca. 712–664 B.C.)
Gold filled with plaster?;
h. ⅜ in. (1.4 cm), w. ½ in. (1.3 cm)
Gift of Edward S. Harkness, 1914
14.7.20

Rams symbolized fertility in ancient Egypt, and so they were associated with several gods whose roles had to do with creation. One of these was Amun-Re, who became the king of the gods in the New Kingdom. Amun-Re was represented by a ram with horns that curl alongside its face, so this amulet may depict him.

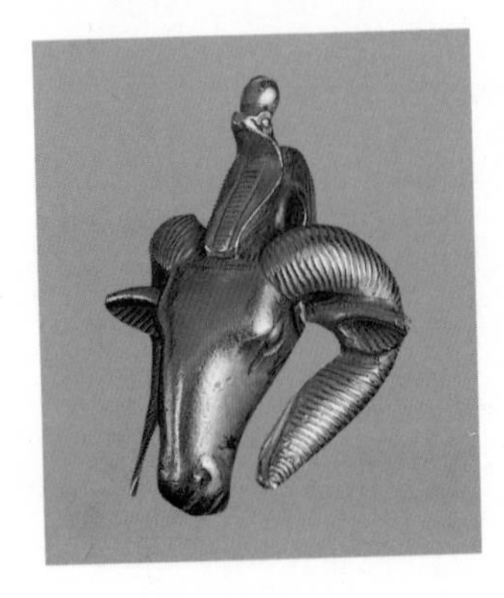

Ram's Head Amulet
Dynasty XXV,
(ca. 712–664 B.C.)
Gold; h. 1⅝ in. (4.2 cm),
w. 1⅜ in. (3.6 cm)
Gift of Norbert Schimmel
Trust, 1989
1989.281.98

Ram amulets make good earrings. Try making a necklace with several of them.

ROSETTE

This floral shape was used as a decorative form over a long period of time. The Egyptians used it in hair and clothing ornaments, for necklace beads, and as a design in jewelry. Its exact meaning is unknown, but all plants were seen as symbols of life. Also, the round shape of the rosette links it to the sun disk, so the rosette might also represent Re, the sun god.

ROSETTE MOLD
Malqata
Dynasty XVIII, reign of Amenhotep III
(ca. 1391–1353 B.C.)
Ceramic; diam. 1$\frac{7}{8}$ in. (4.9 cm)
Rogers Fund, 1911
11.215.690

Lady Senebtisi's Circlet with Rosette Ornaments
Lisht, Tomb of Senebtisi; Late Dynasty XII–XIII (ca. 1878–1640 B.C.)
Gold; diam. of circlet 8 in. (20.3 cm), diam. of rosettes $\frac{7}{16}$ in. (1.1 cm)
Rogers Fund, 1907 07.227.6–7

The rosette is a good decoration for barrettes or other hair ornaments, bracelets, earrings, or magnets. Because it represents the powerful sun god, the rosette is a good charm to say "Congratulations."

SCARAB

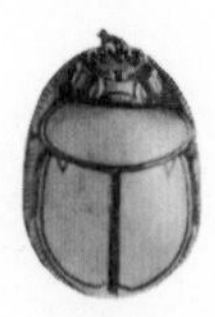

SCARAB
Deir el-Bahri, Foundation Deposit
Dynasty XVIII, reign of Hatshepsut
(ca. 1473–1458 B.C.)
Glazed steatite;
l. 11/16 in. (1.8 cm),
w. 1/2 in. (1.3 cm)
Rogers Fund, 1927
27.3.177

Scarabs make good decorations for rings, picture frames, or magnets. Using a pencil or a toothpick, inscribe your initials or a secret symbol on the bottom of the scarab.

The scarab beetle is probably the best-known ancient Egyptian amulet. It was an important symbol of rebirth, because the Egyptians associated aspects of its behavior with the sun, creator of life. The scarab beetle collects animal dung for food, and then by pushing the dung with its legs, creates large balls, which it delivers to its burrow. The beetle pushing a ball gave the Egyptians a way to explain how the sun moved across the sky: It was pushed by a giant scarab beetle.

The scarab beetle also lays its eggs inside a ball of dung so that its offspring can have a meal immediately after birth. When the eggs hatch, the little beetles crawl out of the ball. To the Egyptians, it looked as if the beetles were created inside the ball, again reminding them o Re, the sun god who was the source of all life.

In the Middle Kingdom, the scarab became very common as a back decoration for name seals. In the New Kingdom and later, the scarab beetle also decorated bracelets, rings, and pectorals and was often placed among a mummy's wrappings.

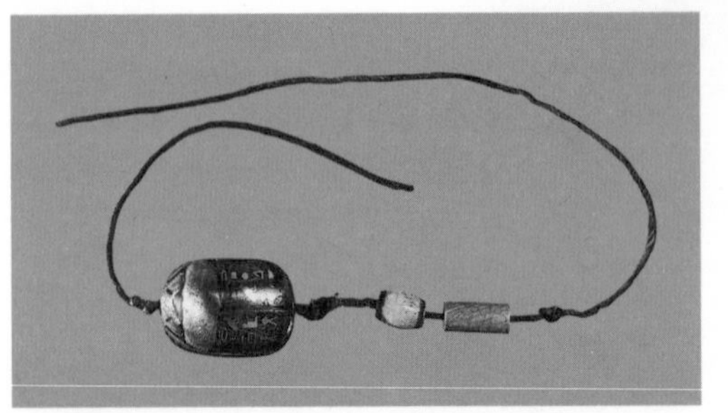

Wah's Inlaid Silver Scarab, on String
Thebes, Early Dynasty XII, reign of Amenemhet I
(ca. 1991–1962 B.C.)
Silver with gold, linen, glazed steatite; scarab
l. 1 1/2 in. (3.85 cm), w. 1 in. (2.65 cm)
Rogers Fund, 1940 40.3.12

This charm depicts one shell of a bivalve (a mollusk with two shells), probably an oyster.

Oyster shell amulets were common during the Middle Kingdom and seem to be most often associated with women. Genuine shells were used as amulets, or their shapes were made in gold or even faience. We know from statuettes and wall paintings that shell amulets were worn around the neck. They were also used to decorate girdles or hip beads. Inscriptions found on certain coffins call this amulet *wedja*, meaning healthy, sound, or whole.

SHELL

OYSTER (?) SHELL PENDANT
Lisht North, Tomb 754
Late Dynasty XII
(ca. 1850–1800 B.C.)
Gold; l. 1 in. (2.5 cm)
Rogers Fund, 1907
07.227.18

Lady Dedetamun Wearing a Silver Shell Amulet at Her Throat
Asasif, East of Pasaba, 6A Radim
Dynasty XII
(ca. 1991–1783 B.C.)
Wood, paint, silver; h. 7½ in. (19 cm)
Rogers Fund, 1919
19.3.1

Use shells for pendants, key rings, or belt decorations. Since the shell means "healthy," it is a good charm to say "Get Well."

TAWERET

TAWERET MOLD
Malqata
Dynasty XVIII, reign of Amenhotep III
(ca. 1391–1353 B.C.)
Ceramic; h. 1 11/16 in. (4.2 cm),
w. 1 1/16 in. (2.8 cm)
Rogers Fund, 1912
12.180.388

Taweret is a powerful goddess with body parts of several different animals. Shown standing upright with human posture and looking pregnant, she has the head and body of a hippopotamus and the paws of a lion. Down her back are scales melding into a tail, details borrowed from the crocodile. Such a combination of parts taken from powerful and terrifying animals made Taweret a potent goddess.

Like the Bes-image, Taweret was most popular with ordinary people and had only a small role in the state-sponsored religion. She was sacred to pregnant women, protecting them from the dangers of childbirth. In this role, her image was used as an amulet not only in jewelry, but also to decorate many household objects.

Taweret Displaying
the Hieroglyph *Sa*,
Meaning Protection
Ptolemaic Period
(304–30 B.C.)
Glass; h. 4 3/8 in. (11 cm)
Purchase, Edward S.
Harkness Gift, 1926
26.7.1193

Make a necklace of Tawerets or use them to decorate a picture frame.

TYET

This amulet represents a strip of cloth that has been looped and knotted. The cloth's original purpose, however, is not known. The amulet is often called the "girdle of Isis," and a spell in the *Book of the Dead* clearly associates this shape with the goddess Isis. When used correctly, the *tyet* called forth the strength of this deity, a powerful magician and the wife and sister of Osiris, lord of the underworld.

The earliest *tyet* amulets, from the New Kingdom, are made of red stones, possibly representing a connection with the female body and blood. Rapidly, however, glass and faience became the most common materials for this popular funerary amulet.

Spell: "You have your blood, O Isis; you have power, O Isis; you have your magic, O Isis. This amulet will protect the Great One, which will drive away whoever will hurt him."

TYET
Dynasty XXVI–XXX
(ca. 664–332 B.C.)
Faience; h. 1⅞ in. (4.7 cm), w. ⅝ in. (1.5 cm)
Gift of Joseph W. Drexel, 1889
89.2.638

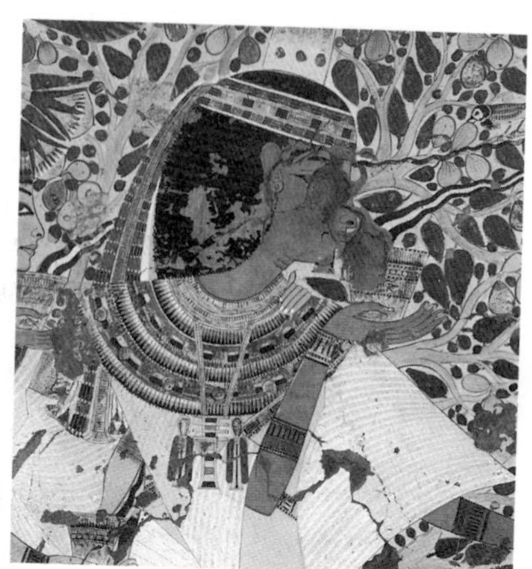

Userhat Wearing a Pectoral with *Djed* and *Tyet* Amulets
Detail from a facsimile of a wall painting from the tomb of Userhat. Sheikh abd el-Qurna, Dynasty XIX, reign of Sety I (ca. 1294–1279 B.C.)
Rogers Fund, 1930
30.4.33

The tyet *makes a good pin, pendant, or magnet.*

WEDJET-EYE

WEDJET-EYE
Ptolemaic Period (304–30 B.C.)
Faience; h. 23/32 in. (1.9 cm),
w. 3/4 in. (2 cm)
Gift of Joseph W. Drexel, 1889
89.2.415

This amulet represents a human eye wearing eyeliner. A thick straight line and a long thin curled line extend below the eye. Egyptologists believe these lines represent the markings of a falcon, a bird sacred to Horus, the king of the gods. Horus was often depicted as a human with a falcon's head, so this human eye with falcon markings is said to stand for one of his eyes. This eye had been injured in a fierce battle that Horus waged against his wicked brother Seth, but later on, it was healed. *Wedjet* actually means "the sound [whole or healthy] eye." Thus, the *wedjet*-eye was a powerful charm for protection against evil happenings.

The earliest examples of *wedjet*-eyes are known from the first age of pyramid building. This charm was popular throughout the rest of Egyptian history and was common in jewelry adorning mummies. Most frequently used in bracelets, the *wedjet*-eye was also suspended on necklaces.
Although *wedjet*-eye amulets were made in many different materials, turquoise-colored faience was the favorite material.

Use wedjet-*eyes on necklaces, rings, and magnets; or glue several to your sunglasses to help protect your eyes. The* wedjet-*eye is a good all-purpose amulet. It can mean good luck as well as protection.*

Ring Decorated with a *Wedjet*-eye
Ptolemaic Period (304–30 B.C.)
Faience; diam. 13/16 in. (2.3 cm)
Gift of Edward S. Harkness, 1926
26.7.804

HOW TO MAKE AMULETS

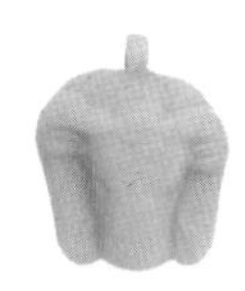

Many Egyptian amulets were made of faience, a hard ceramic material. To make amulets from faience, the ancient Egyptians most often employed molds in the manufacturing process. An amulet mold was made by pressing the desired shape, which had been carved in a hard stone, into wet clay, being careful to make an impression that was even and smooth. The original was removed and the clay was baked. Afterwards, the craftsman would press faience paste, a mixture of ground quartz, natural salts, and water, into the newly created mold. Since the mold had only one side, a so-called open mold, the amulet's back was left plain or shaped by hand. The dried charm was then fired, bringing to the surface faience's characteristic bright blue color. When you make amulets with this kit, you'll use a process similar to the ancient one!

This symbol, a hieroglyph meaning fire or hot, means you need to ask a grown-up for help.

ABOUT THIS KIT

This kit includes a mold with 24 different amulet shapes, polymer clay in three colors, and metal backings to make pins, earrings, rings, necklaces, magnets, and more. You will also need a glass baking dish and an oven for baking your amulets.

You may also need a pointed object like a pencil or a toothpick for making holes, a kitchen knife for cutting simple shapes, wax paper or brown paper to cover your work surface, and a rolling pin for rolling out clay. You may also need white glue or craft glue to stick amulets onto paper, cloth, or plastic.

POLYMER CLAY

You are probably familiar with modeling clay, a natural material made of tiny bits of sand and water. Polymer clay is a kind of plastic. It is very easy to work with and it comes already colored, so you don't have to paint it. To harden it, you bake it in an ordinary oven or a toaster oven *(not a microwave)*. It doesn't shrink or change color when it bakes. When you've used up the clay provided in this kit, you can buy more at craft stores or some toy stores. Or see page 62 for ideas and recipes for other modeling materials.

Polymer clay is sometimes a little stiff when you first start to work with it. Just knead it with your fingers until it becomes soft enough to shape. Don't try adding water to soften it; it won't work. If it is too soft, you can put it in the refrigerator or freezer for a few minutes. Although it doesn't harden completely until you bake it, it's a good idea to store unused clay in an airtight container or wrapped in plastic wrap.

SAFETY

Polymer clay is nontoxic. That means it is safe to use. You should not eat it, though! You also should not use it to make anything that will come in contact with food or drinks. Don't put the clay directly on tables or counters that are used for eating or preparing food, or on good furniture or upholstery. It's a good idea to tape some wax paper or brown paper to your work surface.

You may want to set aside a special baking dish and utensils just for working with the clay. If not, wash any items you've used with lots of soap and hot water before using them for food. And always wash your hands thoroughly after using the clay.

COLORS

This kit comes with clay in colors that might have been used for amulets in ancient Egypt. You can buy polymer clay in lots of different colors. And you can mix colors by blending different colors together. Just work two pieces of clay together for a while until they are blended. For example, the Egyptians frequently used an orange-red stone called carnelian. If you mix one part of red clay and two parts of yellow together, you'll make a color that looks like carnelian. Mix yellow and turquoise to make green, or mix red and turquoise to make purple.

Since the colors do blend easily, you may want to wash or wipe your hands between colors. And don't forget to wash your hands when you're finished.

MAKING AMULETS

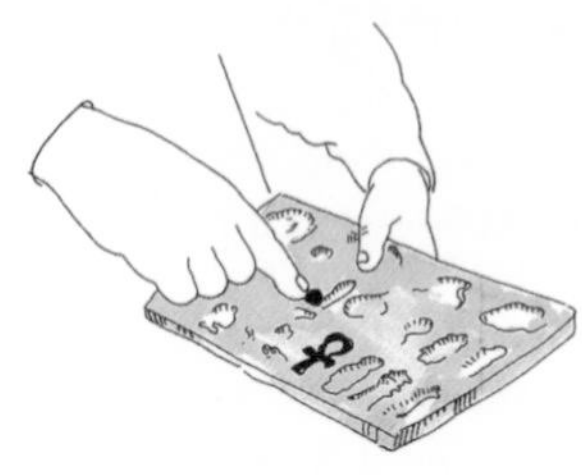

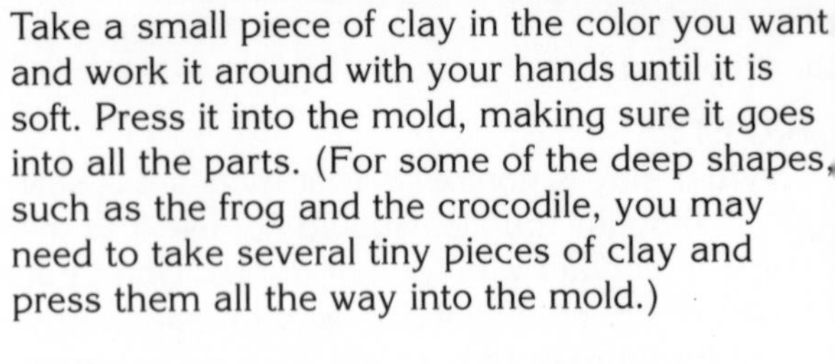

Take a small piece of clay in the color you want and work it around with your hands until it is soft. Press it into the mold, making sure it goes into all the parts. (For some of the deep shapes, such as the frog and the crocodile, you may need to take several tiny pieces of clay and press them all the way into the mold.)

Then pop the amulet out by pressing on the bottom of the mold. If it doesn't come out right, you can shape it a little by hand, or just stick it back into the mold and try again. Remember, until the clay is baked, you can mush it up and reuse it as much as you want.

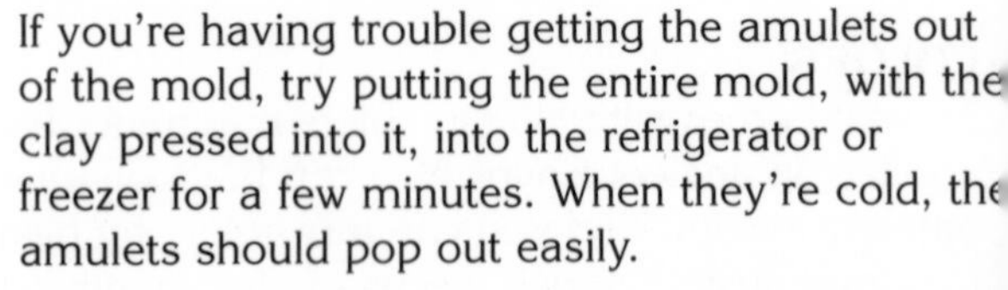

If you're having trouble getting the amulets out of the mold, try putting the entire mold, with the clay pressed into it, into the refrigerator or freezer for a few minutes. When they're cold, the amulets should pop out easily.

If you are planning to string the amulet, you may want to put a hole into it before you bake it. Use a pointed object like a pencil or a toothpick. Poke the pointed object in one side where you want the hole to be, and twist it gently until it is about to come through the other side. Then take your pointed object out and twist it in the other side.

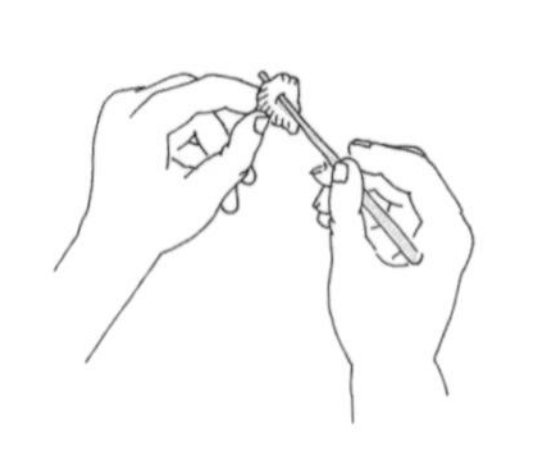

If you are joining two or more pieces, be sure to work them together well before baking.

You can bake metal or glass items right into the clay; just be sure that they can be baked.

Ask a grown-up for help if you don't know whether or not something can go in the oven. Plastic, paper, and other non-bakeable items can be glued on after baking.

HANDY SHAPES

You may want to use these shapes when you're making amulets into things.

BALLS. Roll a lump of clay around between your hands until it is nice and smooth. You can make a ball first before pressing clay into the mold. A flattened-out ball makes a good base for an amulet.

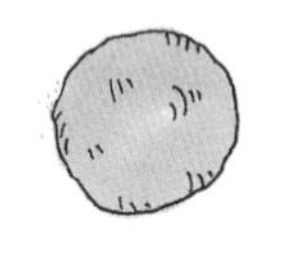

ROPES. Roll the clay between your palms until it makes a rope shape. Ropes are handy for making rings or bracelets.

SHEETS. Put a lump of clay between two sheets of wax paper and roll it with a rolling pin until it is flat and smooth. You can then cut it into shapes with a kitchen knife. (Ask an adult to help you if you are using a sharp knife.) Sheets are good for making things like picture frames.

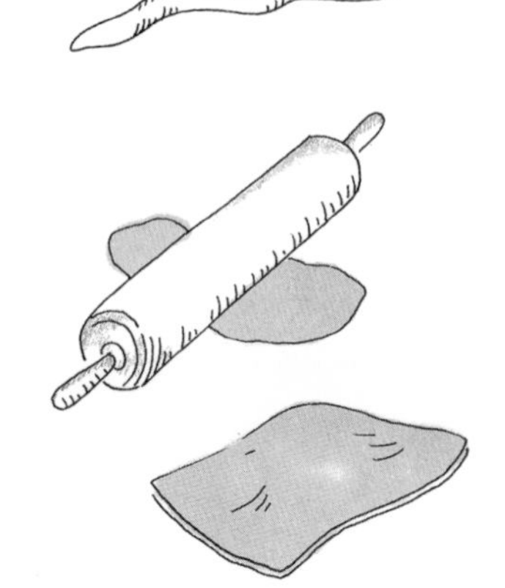

SOME TIPS

STRIPES

To create a striped effect, make thin ropes in different colors. Put them into the mold side by side. Press them together, then push the amulet out of the mold.

MARBLEIZING

Make two or more ropes in different colors. Twist them together. Mush the ropes until the colors start to blend. Then use the marbleized clay in the mold.

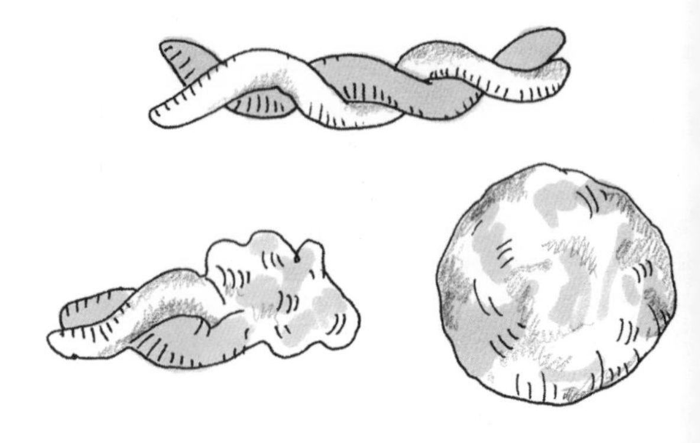

DECORATIONS

Use tiny balls for eyes or dots.

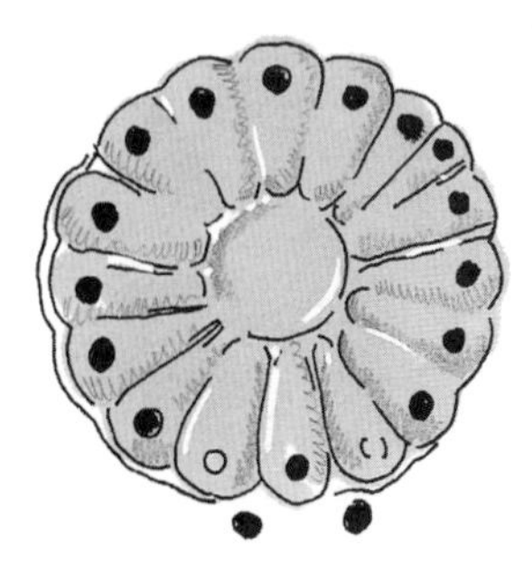

Use thin ropes as accents.

BAKING!

Be sure to have a grown-up help you any time you use an oven.

You can bake your finished amulets in a regular oven or a toaster oven. Do not use a microwave oven. Place them on a glass, ovenproof baking dish, and bake in a preheated 275°F (135°C, gas mark 1) oven. It's a good idea to check your oven temperature with an oven thermometer. Don't bake the clay at a higher temperature. Your amulets will not turn out right, and the high temperature could release some unpleasant fumes.

The clay should be baked for 15 minutes for each ¼ inch (0.6 cm) of thickness. Most of the amulets will be done in 15 to 20 minutes. Be sure to use potholders when taking the baking dish out. The amulets are very hot when they first come out of the oven, so wait until they are cool to take them off the dish. Also, they harden a little more as they cool, and they may break before they're completely hardened. Remember to wash the baking dish thoroughly before using it for food.

You may smell a plasticky smell when the clay is baking. Be sure the room where you're baking is well ventilated. Open a window or turn on the oven fan if you're baking a lot. If you do burn any of the clay, turn off the oven and take the clay outside until it cools.

REMEMBER

- Cover your work surface with wax paper or brown paper
- Work the clay around with your hands to make it soft and flexible
- Bake your amulets on a glass, ovenproof dish at 275°F (135°C, gas mark 1)
- Bake your amulets for 15 minutes for each quarter inch (0.6 cm) of thickness
- Bake metal and glass objects right into the clay; attach other objects with glue after amulets have been baked and cooled
- Ask an adult for help with the oven and when using sharp objects
- Wash your hands and any utensils you have used when you're finished

WHAT TO MAKE WITH AMULETS

On the pages that follow are suggestions and instructions for making specific things with your amulets. Be creative and come up with your own ideas, too.

DECORATE WITH AMULETS

You can glue amulets onto lots of things. Just check with a grown-up before you put them onto household items, and don't use them on anything that comes into contact with food or drink or that might get wet.

Here are some things you might glue amulets onto:

- barrettes
- boxes
- caps
- flowerpots
- greeting cards
- keys
- picture frames
- sunglasses

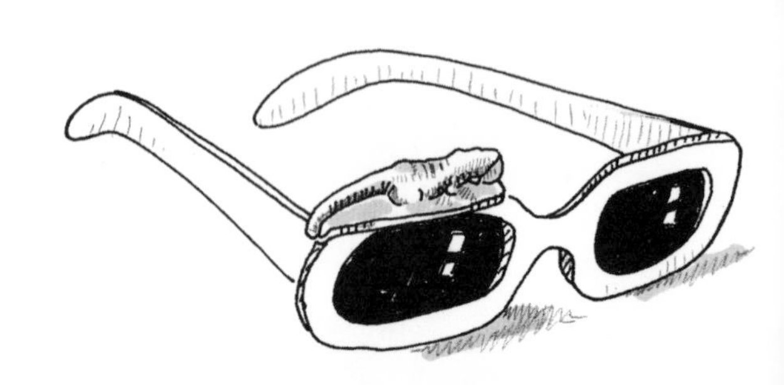

THREE-DIMENSIONAL AMULETS

The molds for the baboon and the cat are in two parts. If you want a flat shape to glue onto something or to use with a pin or magnet backing, you can make just the front of the baboon or one side of the cat. Or you can make three-dimensional figures.

Make both front and back halves of the baboon amulet or both halves of the cat. Remove them from the mold and gently press them together. If the details become blurry when you press, you can put the amulet back into the mold for a few seconds.

Some of the other molds are symmetrical, or the same on both sides. You can make two of the same amulet and stick them together, too. Try it with the Bes-image, the *ankh,* the papyrus scepter, the *djed*-pillar, the *tyet*, or the heart.

PENCIL TOP

A baboon amulet might inspire you when you're writing or doing homework!

Make both front and back halves of the baboon amulet. Remove them from the mold and gently press them together. If the details become blurry when you press, you can put the amulet back into the mold for a few seconds.

Take the eraser off a pencil. Then press the eraser end into the bottom of the amulet, twisting gently until the pencil is about halfway into the amulet.

Remove the pencil and bake the amulet for 25 minutes.

When the amulet is completely cool, place it back on the end of the pencil. You may need a couple of drops of glue to help hold it in place.

RINGS

There are two ways to make rings.

Using a ring backing, press the backing into the amulet, adding a small flat piece of clay on the back to keep it in place. Make sure the clay is worked together, then bake.

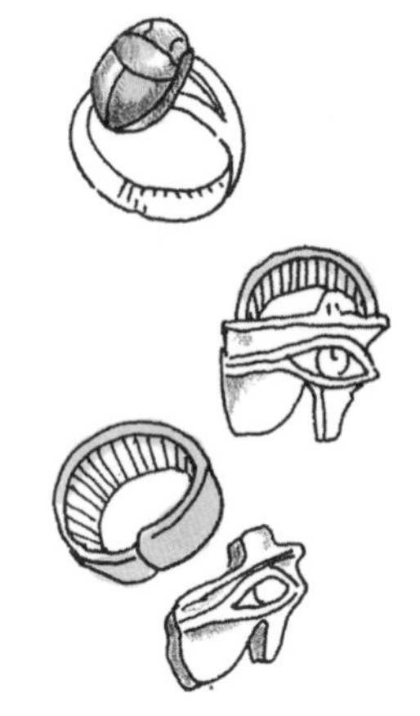

Make your own ring backing. Make a thin rope of clay, long enough to go around your finger. Flatten the rope, then form it into a circle. Add an amulet shape over the seam where the ends meet. Work the clay together well so it won't break. Bake.

PINS AND TIE TACKS

Gently press a pin backing into the back of the amulet. You can also use a safety pin. Add a small, flat piece of clay to keep the backing in place. Make sure the clay is worked together so it won't come apart. Then bake.

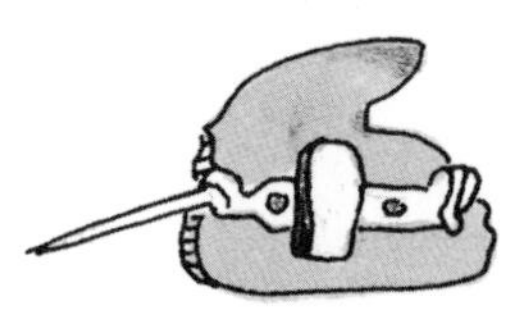

Try leaving the amulet in the mold while you're adding the backing. It will help the amulet keep its shape while you mush the clay together.

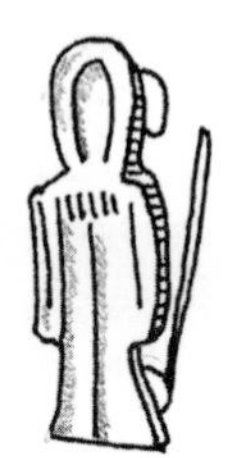

PENDANTS

There are several ways to make pendants.

You can make a small hole in an amulet with a toothpick or a pencil before baking it. After baking, thread cord through the hole.

Or you can press a jewelry hook into the top of the amulet, then bake. Thread cord through the hook to make a necklace. You may want to make a knot in the cord where it attaches to the hook.

Press two *ankhs* together back-to-back before baking to make a three-dimensional pendant. After baking, you can thread cord right through the top loop of the *ankh*.

BRACELETS

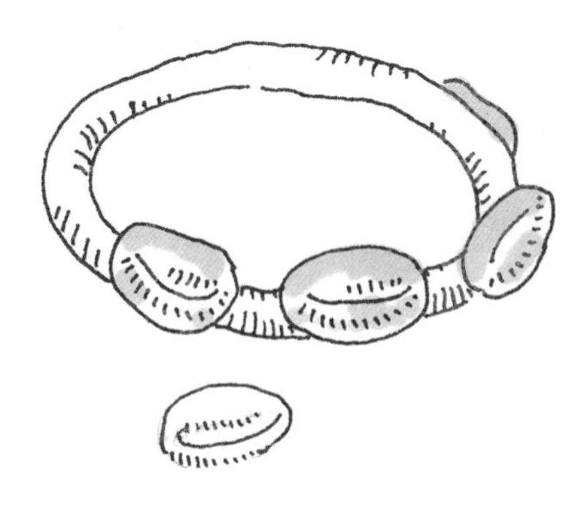

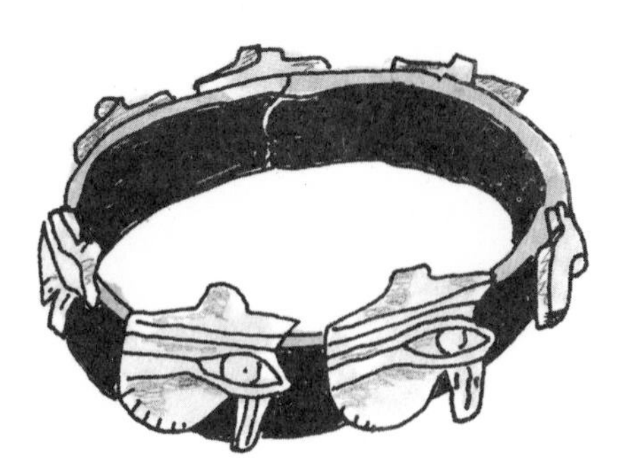

You can make a bangle bracelet using just clay. Make a rope long enough to go around your wrist. Be sure it can fit over your hand, too. Join the ends together to make a circular shape. Add amulets to the bracelet, then bake.

You could also flatten the rope before you put the amulets on.

Make several amulets, either using jewelry hooks or making holes in each one, then bake them. When they've cooled, lay them out on a table to find an arrangement you like. Then thread them onto cord. Make a knot in the cord where the hook is, or you can make knots on either side of each of the amulets to hold them in place. Remember that knots themselves had magical powers for the Egyptians.

CHARM BRACELETS AND NECKLACES

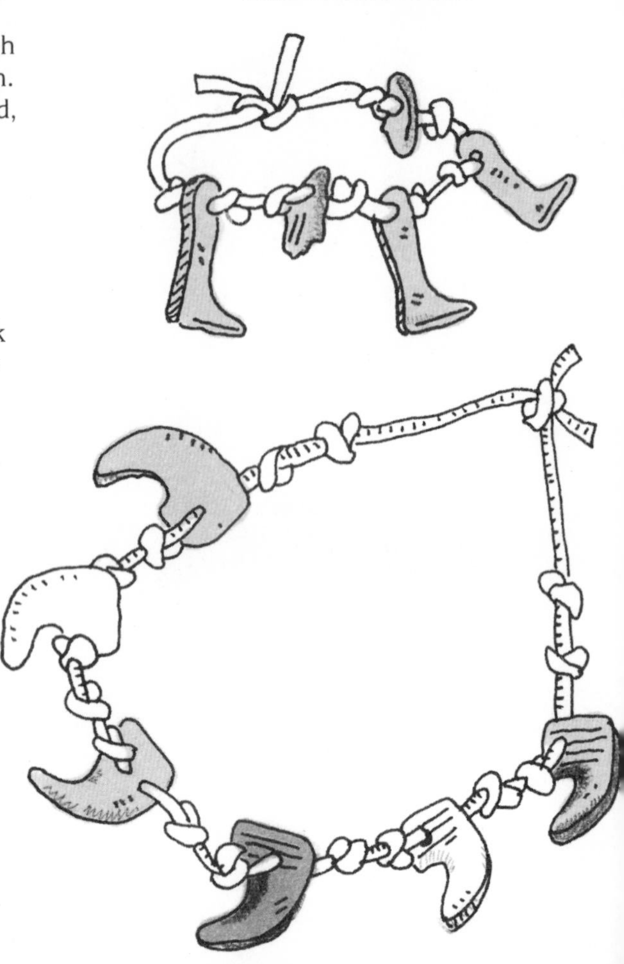

FRIENDSHIP CHARM BRACELET

You may have heard about friendship quilts, in which each square is made by a different person and given to a friend, perhaps for a wedding present. You and your friends can make friendship charm bracelets with amulets. With a group of friends, each person can make one amulet. Then you put them together on a bracelet to give to someone. Your amulet could be made in your favorite color, or it could be an animal or shape that is special to you—maybe you love frogs or collect shells. Or the amulet could represent something you wish for your friend: a hand for creativity, or a *wedjet*-eye for protection. Bake the amulets and make them into a charm bracelet for your friend.

EARRINGS

To make clip earrings, press the earring backs gently into the amulet. If you're using a large amulet, you can add a little clay to hold the backing in place. Bake.

To use earring wires, press a jewelry hook into the top of the amulet, then bake. Attach the earring wire through the hole in the hook.

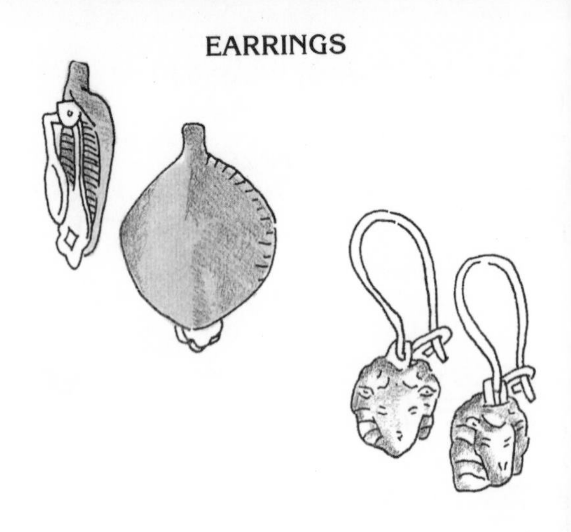

MAGNETS

Cut off a piece of the magnetic strip and glue it to the back of a baked amulet.

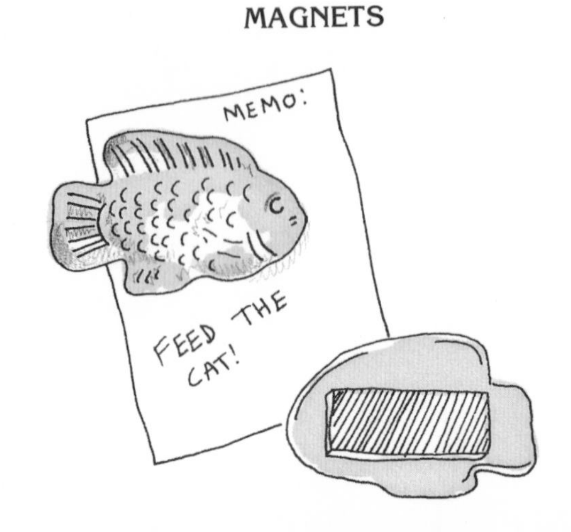

THUMBTACKS OR DRAWING PINS

Press the back of a thumbtack or metal drawing pin into the amulet before baking. Be careful not to prick yourself! Stick the pointy end of the tack into a small wad of aluminum foil so you can bake it right side up.

KEYS

Cover the top part of a key with a thin sheet of clay. Decorate with amulets, then bake. Be sure there's room for the teeth of the key to go into its lock.

KEY RINGS

Decorate a key ring with an amulet. You can bake amulets onto a metal key ring or use glue to attach them to a plastic one. Or you can bake a jewelry hook into an amulet and attach it to a key or key ring with cord or ribbon.

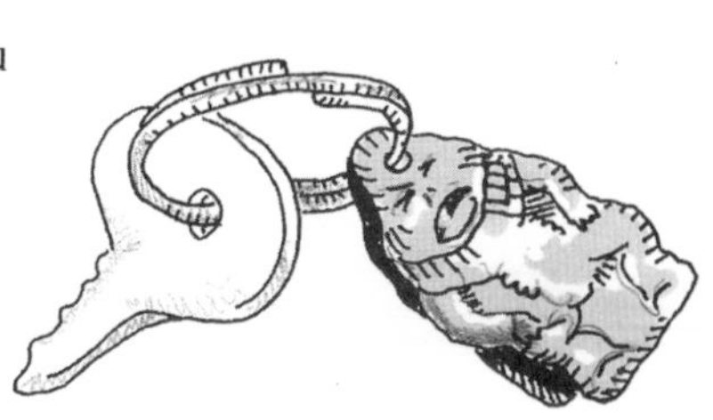

BARRETTES

Make a thin sheet of clay and cover the top of a metal barrette with it, pressing the clay over the edge to hold it in place. (Be sure the barrette still opens and shuts.) Add amulets, pressing them gently but firmly into the clay so they will stay in place. Then bake.

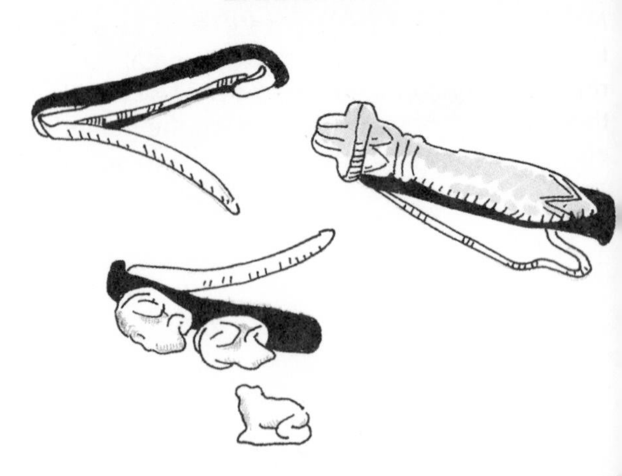

PONYTAIL HOLDERS

Make an amulet with a jewelry hook attached. After baking, attach a thin ribbon through the hole on the hook.

You could also glue an amulet onto a ponytail holder.

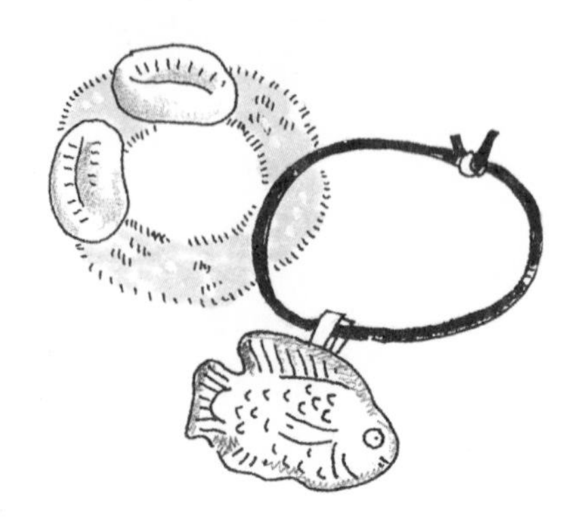

NAPKIN RINGS

Make a thick rope, then join the ends together to make a circle shape. You can flatten the rope if you want to. Decorate with amulets, then bake.

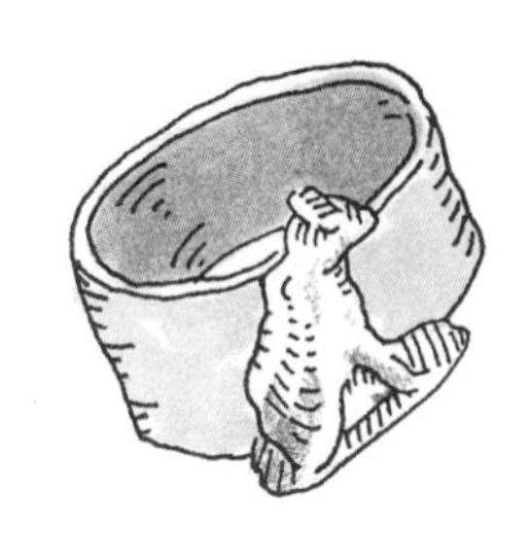

SHOELACES

Run faster and jump higher! Make four of the foot or hare amulets. Make a hole in each one, then bake.

When the amulets are completely cooled, string the ends of your shoelaces through the holes. (Be sure your shoes are laced first.) Make knots on each side of the amulets to hold them in place.

PAPER CLIP

Press the smaller end of a paper clip into an amulet, then bake. Be sure that enough of the paper clip is exposed so it will still clip.

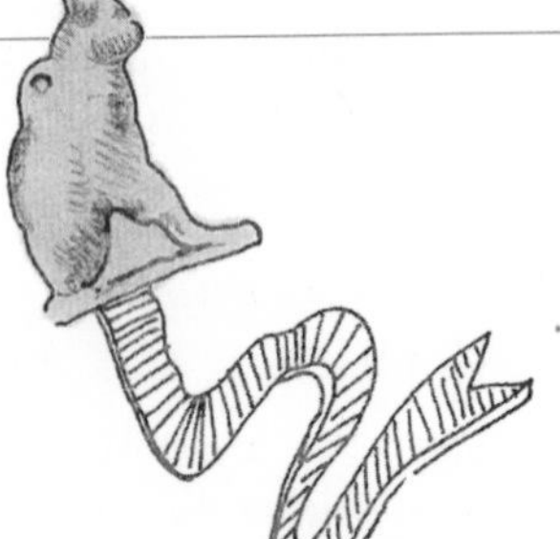

BOOKMARK

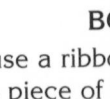

You can use a ribbon, about 12 inches (30 cm) long, or a piece of colored paper about 1 inch wide and 10 inches long (2.5 x 25 cm). Glue an amulet on the top to help you keep your place in a book.

MAGIC WAND

Use a popsicle stick, a chopstick, or other stick. Press the end of it into a unbaked amulet. Remove the stick and bake the amulet. You can use markers or paint to decorate the stick while the amulet is baking. When the amulet is cool, place it back on the end of the stick, using a little glue. Then add ribbons or other decorations.

DIORAMA

Many of the amulets represent animals that lived in ancient Egypt. Use a shoebox or a piece of folded cardboard or poster board to make a background. Use markers, paints, or crayons to draw an Egyptian scene. Then place baboons, cats, fish, crocodiles, frogs, or ibises into your diorama.

SURPRISE BALL

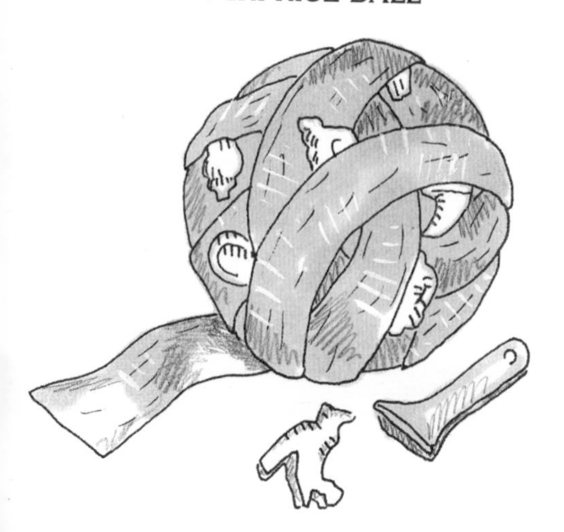

Make about 15 or 20 amulets and bake them. Then take a roll of crepe paper. Wrap the paper a couple of times around one amulet, then put another amulet in and wrap more paper around. Keep going until you have a crepe paper ball full of amulets. Give it to a friend and see how much fun it is to unwrap!

PICTURE FRAME

Cut a piece of cardboard about one inch (2.5 cm) bigger than the picture you want to frame. Fold the cardboard in half. Beginning at the folded side, cut out a rectangle, leaving one inch (2.5 cm) on the three outer edges.

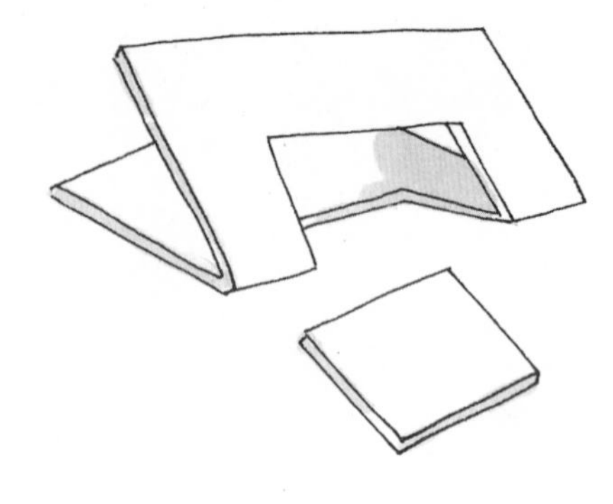

Now open up the cardboard. Color it with paint or markers. Then glue amulets onto it. (Try to cover up the fold lines.)

Cut another piece of cardboard a little smaller than the frame. Put the picture you are framing behind the frame, and tape the second piece of cardboard onto the back to hold it in place.

You can punch holes in the top of the frame and hang it up with a ribbon or yarn.

To make the frame stand up, cut a triangle out of cardboard. The height of the triangle should be the same height as the frame. Fold the triangle in half and glue or tape half of the triangle onto the back of the frame.

GREETING CARDS, INVITATIONS, AND STATIONERY

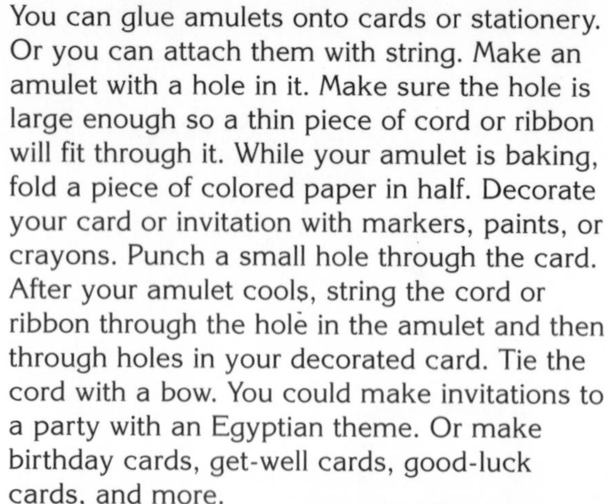

You can glue amulets onto cards or stationery. Or you can attach them with string. Make an amulet with a hole in it. Make sure the hole is large enough so a thin piece of cord or ribbon will fit through it. While your amulet is baking, fold a piece of colored paper in half. Decorate your card or invitation with markers, paints, or crayons. Punch a small hole through the card. After your amulet cools, string the cord or ribbon through the hole in the amulet and then through holes in your decorated card. Tie the cord with a bow. You could make invitations to a party with an Egyptian theme. Or make birthday cards, get-well cards, good-luck cards, and more.

HAVE AN AMULET PARTY

Have an Egyptian party. Use amulets to make invitations, place cards, decorations, presents, and thank-you notes.
You could even have an amulet party and make friendship bracelets for each person there!

AN AMULET PARTY

SAY IT WITH AMULETS

GOOD LUCK
Wedjet-eye:
an all-purpose amulet that can mean good luck
Baboon and Ibis:
good luck for taking a test
Foot:
good luck for a sports event
Djed-pillar:
"endurance" and "strength" for running a marathon

HAPPY BIRTHDAY
Ankh: "long life"

CONGRATULATIONS
Scarab and rosette:
the sun god, meaning "power"
Ankh: "long life"

GET WELL
Wedjet-eye:
"sound" or "whole"
Shell: "healthy"
Hand or foot:
healing for an injury to those parts
Papyrus scepter:
"green" meaning "health"

PROTECTION FOR TRAVEL, ETC.
Bes: protection

ADDITIONAL SUPPLIES

You can buy more jewelry backings at craft stores or bead stores. Experiment with odds and ends around your house.

If you run out of the polymer clay included with this kit, you can buy more at craft stores or some toy stores. Look for Sculpey III® or Fimo Soft®. Be sure to follow the baking directions on the package.

You can purchase a set of eight one-ounce blocks of clay in eight different colors from the Museum. The cost is $7.95, plus shipping and handling and applicable sales tax. To order, request Fun with Amulets Supplement Kit (N1051X).

By mail: The Metropolitan Museum of Art
Special Service Office
Middle Village, New York 11381-0001

By telephone: 800-468-7386 (credit card orders only)
(001-800-468-7386 in the U.K.)

By fax: 718-628-5485 (credit card orders only)
(001-718-628-5485 in the U.K.)

You can also use the mold with some other clays. Try it with Play-Doh®, or make your own "play clay." (You cannot bake Play-Doh® or "play clay.")

Play Clay

3 cups (24 oz; .75 litre) of flour
1 cup (8 oz; .25 litre) of salt
1 cup (8 oz; .25 litre) of water
1 tablespoon (1 oz) vegetable oil
food coloring

Mix flour and salt together. Add oil and food color to water. Gradually add liquid to flour mixture until it is stiff. Add more flour if it's still too gooey.

FOR FURTHER READING

Carol Andrews, *Amulets of Ancient Egypt.*
London: British Museum Press; Austin: University of Texas Press, 1994.

Carol Andrews, *Ancient Egyptian Jewelry.*
London: British Museum Publications, 1990, 2nd ed. 1996;
New York: Harry N. Abrams, Inc., 1991.

Sue D'Auria *et al.*, *Mummies and Magic: The Funerary Arts of Ancient Egypt.*
Boston: Museum of Fine Arts, Boston, 1988.

ohn F. Nunn, *Ancient Egyptian Medicine.*
London: British Museum Press;
Norman: University of Oklahoma Press, 1996.

W. M. F. Petrie, *Amulets.* London: Constable & Co., Ltd., 1914.

Geraldine Pinch, *Magic in Ancient Egypt.*
London: British Museum Press; Austin: University of Texas Press, 1994.

S. Quirke, *Ancient Egyptian Religion.*
London: British Museum Press; New York: Dover Publications Inc., 1992.

obert K. Ritner, *The Mechanics of Ancient Egyptian Magical Practice.*
Studies in Ancient Oriental Civilization No. 54.
Chicago: The Oriental Institute of the University of Chicago, 1993.

Produced by the Department of Special Publications,
The Metropolitan Museum of Art
Publishing Manager, Robie Rogge
Editor, Carolyn Vaughan
Production, Laurie Brady
Editorial Assistant, Ilana Greenberg

Models, based on original amulets in the Department of
Egyptian Art, made by Ron Street, Supervisor,
Molding Studio, Three-Dimensional Reproductions,
The Metropolitan Museum of Art

Photography by The Metropolitan Museum of Art
Photograph Studio

Illustrations by Robin Rule
Design by Miriam Berman, with Sophia Stavropoulos